Contents

Are you ready for a challenge?

What is Key Stage 2 ReviseWise?

In May, Year 6 pupils take their Key Stage 2 (KS2) National Tests In English, Maths and Science. The Tests show teachers what level children are working at. This book is part of the BBC's Key Stage 2 ReviseWise service, created to help children get ready to do their best in all their KS2 National Tests.

The KS2 ReviseWise Maths resources are:

- this ReviseWise Challenge quiz book
- the ReviseWise English preparation and practice book
- television programmes that you can video
- videos to buy   • a CD-ROM
- a website http://www.bbc.co.uk.revision

There's such a variety of things to do in ReviseWise that revising need never be boring.

There are even ReviseWise resources for schools, so there's a link between home and school learning.

The ReviseWise Maths resources have been developed and written by specialists to help children aiming to reach level 4 and above (just over half marks in the Maths Tests will achieve level 4). ReviseWise covers the key areas of Maths which will be tested.

How to get the most out of Key Stage 2 ReviseWise

• Help your child to work though the books. There are lots of tips from the ReviseWise owl to help with the answers and give advice.

• Encourage your child to watch (and re-watch) the videos. They bring the subject to life and explain what the Tests are all about.

• Is your child always glued to the computer? The CD-ROM takes children through questions step-by-step, with as much – or as little – help as they need along the way.

• If you're on the Internet, your child can visit the website for more learning fun. There's also a special section to help parents get to grips with the Tests and revision.

Using this book

Each page in this book offers questions, puzzles or activities which will help children confirm what they know and practise their skills in Maths ready for the KS2 Tests. The main points they need to know are highlighted at the top of each page. Each page has three question rounds. Round 1 has four multiple choice questions. Round 2 is a mixture of four different quiz questions. Round three is a challenge question.

Children can work steadily through the book, or head straight for the activities they know they need more practice in. At the end of each page, children can record their progress by marking their score on the pictures running up the right hand side of the page. They can circle or tick the picture showing the number of answers they have got right.

If children do the activities in this book in pencil, they can do them again later, either for repeat practice, or if they get any answers wrong. They can keep track of how much work they have done, and their scores, by filling in the score charts on pages 44 and 45. The questions in Rounds 1 and 2 are worth one point each. The question in Round 3 is worth two points, so there are ten points in total on each page. For Round 3 there may not be two obvious answers. If a child gets it all right, give two marks. If he or she has a go and gets part of it correct, give one mark.

Other resources for ReviseWise Challenge:

English quiz book ISBN 0 563 54218 7

Science quiz book ISBN 0 563 54220 9

English quiz video ISBN 0 563 54224 1

Science quiz video ISBN 0 563 54226 8

If you like, you can agree rewards with your child for successfully completing activities. There is a chart for doing this on pages 44 and 45 of this book.

Multiplying and dividing by 10 and 100

To multiply by 100, move all the digits two places to the left.

The empty place is filled with a zero.

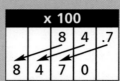

x 100			
	8	4	.7
8	4	7	0

To divide by 100, move all the digits two places to the right.

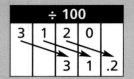

÷ 100			
3	1	2	0
		3	1	.2

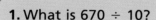 **Round 1** Circle the correct answer for each of these.

When you multiply and divide by 10 and 100, it's the digits that move not the decimal point.

1. 34 × 10 equals   a) 3400   b) 3.4   c) 340

2. 470 ÷ 10 equals   a) 47   b) 4.7   c) 4700

3. 7.6 × 100 equals   a) 76   b) 7600   c) 760

4. 802 ÷ 100 equals   a) 8.02   b) 80.2   c) 802

Round 2

1. What is 670 ÷ 10? ☐

2. What is 1.9 × 100? ☐

3. Write the missing number:

   45.8 × ☐ = 4580

4. Write the missing number:

   372 ÷ ☐ = 3.72

 10

 9

8

 7

6

5

4

3

2

1

Round 3

Spot the mistakes.

Circle the incorrect numbers coming out of the bag.

 *Worth 2 points*

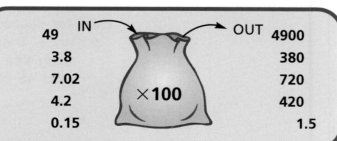

IN		OUT
49		4900
3.8		380
7.02	×100	720
4.2		420
0.15		1.5

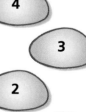

Ordering numbers

To help work out the order of numbers, you can write them in a list.

26108
2790
38
2.85
2.6

Make sure you line up the units column

< less than
> greater than

These numbers are written in order, starting with the smallest. Which number is in the wrong place. Circle the answer.

Read the numbers aloud to help you.

1.   732   743   747   739   758
a) 743   b) 739   c) 758

2.   4830   4803   4840   4841   4904
a) 4840   b) 4904   c) 4803

3.   62180 6380 6488 6500 62250
a) 62250   b) 62180 c) 6500

4.   2.37   2.4   2.39   2.51   2.6
a) 2.4   b) 2.51   c) 2.39

Write these sets of numbers in the correct order, starting with the smallest number.

241   214   311   301   271
1. ☐ ☐ ☐ ☐ ☐

62051 63001 6251 60520 61205
2. ☐ ☐ ☐ ☐ ☐

4810   4180   4208   4080   4111
3. ☐ ☐ ☐ ☐ ☐

6.4   6.45   7.7   6.8   7.21
4. ☐ ☐ ☐ ☐ ☐

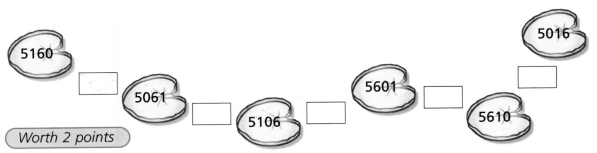

Write < or > between the numbers to complete the line of lily pads.

5160 ☐ 5061 ☐ 5106 ☐ 5601 ☐ 5610 ☐ 5016

Worth 2 points

Estimating and rounding numbers

When you round numbers to the nearest 10 or 100 the halfway position is important. Halfway points are always rounded up.

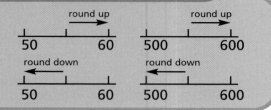

Round 1   Circle the correct numbers.

Decide whether to round up or round down.

1. Which number rounds to 60 to the nearest ten?	2. Which number rounds to 300 to the nearest hundred?	3. Which number rounds to 2600 to the nearest hundred?	4. Which number rounds to 3 to the nearest whole number?
a) 54	a) 248	a) 2480	a) 2.08
b) 68	b) 340	b) 2565	b) 3.6
c) 56	c) 351	c) 2670	c) 2.56

Round 2

Round these sums to the nearest ten to find approximate answers.

1. 77 + 92   2. 417 + 198   3. 545 + 83   4. 204 + 258

Round 3   True or false? Circle your answer.

1. 3845 spectators were at the football match. This is 3900 rounded to the nearest ten.

True/False

Worth 2 points

2. 4074 people visited the museum in May. This is 4000 people rounded to the nearest hundred?

True/False

Negative numbers

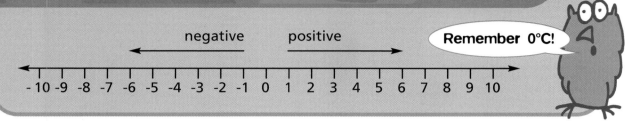

negative   positive

Remember 0°C!

-10 -9 -8 -7 -6 -5 -4 -3 -2 -1 0 1 2 3 4 5 6 7 8 9 10

Round 1 What is the temperature shown on each of these thermometers?

-30 -20 -10 0 10 20 30 40

1. a) 14 °C **b)** 18 °C **c)** 16 °C

-30 -20 -10 0 10 20 30 40

2. a) 3 °C **b)** −3 °C **c)** 6 °C

-30 -20 -10 0 10 20 30 40

3. a) 1 °C **b)** −2 °C **c)** −1 °C

-30 -20 -10 0 10 20 30 40

4. a) −5 °C **b)** −15 °C **c)** −25 °C

Round 2 What are the differences between these temperatures?

1. − 5 °C
  2 °C
  ☐ °C

2. 4 °C
  −1 °C
  ☐ °C

3. − 8 °C
  − 2 °C
  ☐ °C

4. 6 °C
  − 6 °C
  ☐ °C

Round 3 Anty is on the ground floor of Formaria ant city. These are his movements up and down the lift, starting from the ground floor.

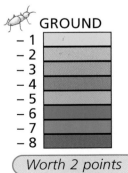

GROUND
− 1
− 2
− 3
− 4
− 5
− 6
− 7
− 8

Worth 2 points

1 Down 2 → **3** Down 3 → **5** Down 4 → **7** Down 5

2 Up 1 → **4** Up 2 → **6** Up 3 → **8** Up 4

1. Which floors does he visit twice? ☐ ☐ ☐ ☐

2. Which floors does he not visit? ☐ ☐ ☐ ☐

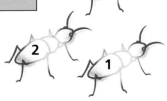

9

Equivalent fractions

Equivalent fractions look different from each other, but are really worth the same.

$$\frac{1}{2} = \frac{2}{4} = \frac{4}{8}$$

$\frac{1}{2}$				$\frac{1}{2}$			
$\frac{1}{4}$		$\frac{1}{4}$		$\frac{1}{4}$		$\frac{1}{4}$	
$\frac{1}{8}$	$\frac{1}{8}$	$\frac{1}{8}$	$\frac{1}{8}$	$\frac{1}{8}$	$\frac{1}{8}$	$\frac{1}{8}$	$\frac{1}{8}$

Round 1 Circle the equivalent fractions.

Can you get them all right?

1. $\frac{2}{3}$ a) $\frac{5}{6}$ b) $\frac{7}{12}$ c) $\frac{4}{6}$ | 2. $\frac{3}{4}$ a) $\frac{6}{8}$ b) $\frac{8}{12}$ c) $\frac{2}{3}$

3. $\frac{1}{4}$ a) $\frac{1}{2}$ b) $\frac{4}{12}$ c) $\frac{2}{8}$ | 4. $\frac{5}{6}$ a) $\frac{2}{3}$ b) $\frac{9}{12}$ c) $\frac{10}{12}$

10

9

8

7

Round 2 These pairs of pizzas have the same amount left. What is the fraction left for each one?

1. = ☐/☐

2. = ☐/☐

3. = ☐/☐

4. 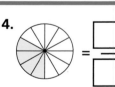 = ☐/☐

6

5

4

Round 3 (Worth 2 points)

Circle the odd one out in each set.

1.
| $\frac{2}{6}$ | $\frac{3}{9}$ | $\frac{5}{15}$ |
| $\frac{3}{12}$ | $\frac{10}{30}$ | $\frac{4}{12}$ |

2.
| $\frac{6}{10}$ | $\frac{15}{25}$ | $\frac{16}{30}$ |
| $\frac{12}{20}$ | $\frac{30}{50}$ | $\frac{9}{15}$ |

3

2

1

Ordering and simplifying fractions

To order fractions, change them so they have the same denominator (bottom number). Look at this example: which is largest out of $\frac{1}{2}$, $\frac{3}{4}$ and $\frac{2}{3}$?

These can all be changed to twelfths: $\frac{6}{12}$, $\frac{9}{12}$, $\frac{8}{12}$

so now you can see that $\frac{3}{4}$ is larger than $\frac{2}{3}$.

 Circle which fraction – a), b) or c) – is the simplified form of the first fraction.

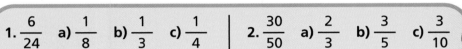

1. $\frac{6}{24}$ a) $\frac{1}{8}$ b) $\frac{1}{3}$ c) $\frac{1}{4}$ | 2. $\frac{30}{50}$ a) $\frac{2}{3}$ b) $\frac{3}{5}$ c) $\frac{3}{10}$

3. $\frac{15}{20}$ a) $\frac{1}{4}$ b) $\frac{3}{5}$ c) $\frac{3}{4}$ | 4. $\frac{10}{15}$ a) $\frac{2}{3}$ b) $\frac{1}{5}$ c) $\frac{3}{10}$

How many questions did you get right? Circle your cake.

 Write these fractions in the correct order. Start with the smallest.

1. $\frac{3}{4}$ $\frac{5}{8}$ $\frac{1}{2}$ $\frac{1}{4}$

2. $\frac{7}{12}$ $\frac{1}{3}$ $\frac{2}{3}$ $\frac{5}{6}$

3. $\frac{4}{5}$ $\frac{7}{10}$ $\frac{3}{5}$ $\frac{8}{15}$

4. $\frac{5}{6}$ $\frac{7}{12}$ $\frac{3}{8}$ $\frac{12}{24}$

 Worth 2 points

That's a lot of presents at Christmas!

Grandma has 4 grandchildren.

David is $\frac{3}{12}$ of her age.

Hannah is $\frac{6}{12}$ of her age.

Ben is $\frac{3}{15}$ of her age.

Kathy is $\frac{8}{30}$ of her age.

1. Which grandchild is the eldest? ☐
2. Which grandchild is the youngest? ☐

10
9
8
7
6
5
4
3
2
1

Improper fractions

$2\dfrac{1}{4}$ is a mixed number. It has a whole number and fractions together.

A mixed number can change to an improper fraction:

$$2\dfrac{1}{4} = \dfrac{8}{4} + \dfrac{1}{4} = \dfrac{9}{4}$$

10

 Circle the correct improper fraction for each mixed number.

1. $1\dfrac{3}{5}$ a) $\dfrac{4}{5}$ b) $\dfrac{6}{5}$ c) $\dfrac{8}{5}$ 2. $2\dfrac{3}{4}$ a) $\dfrac{11}{4}$ b) $\dfrac{5}{4}$ c) $\dfrac{6}{4}$

3. $1\dfrac{2}{3}$ a) $\dfrac{4}{3}$ b) $\dfrac{5}{3}$ c) $\dfrac{6}{3}$ 4. $3\dfrac{5}{6}$ a) $\dfrac{15}{3}$ b) $\dfrac{23}{6}$ c) $\dfrac{18}{6}$

 Fill in the missing numbers.

1. $\dfrac{\square}{5} = 2\dfrac{4}{5}$ 2. $\dfrac{14}{3} = 4\dfrac{\square}{3}$

3. $\dfrac{\square}{4} = 5\dfrac{3}{4}$ 4. $\dfrac{7}{2} = 3\dfrac{\square}{2}$

How many planes did you get?

 Match one mouse to each computer.

 $3\dfrac{5}{6}$  $3\dfrac{4}{5}$

$\dfrac{21}{5}$

$\dfrac{23}{6}$ $\dfrac{21}{6}$ $\dfrac{30}{6}$

$\dfrac{19}{5}$ $\dfrac{23}{5}$

Worth 2 points

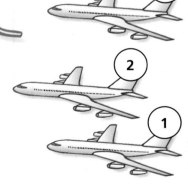

Fractions and decimals

To change fractions to decimals divide the numerator by the denominator.

numerator $\dfrac{1}{4}$ → $1 \div 4 = 0.25$
denominator

To change decimals to fractions change them to tenths or hundreths.

$0.4 = \dfrac{4}{10} = \dfrac{2}{5}$　　　$0.65 = \dfrac{65}{100} = \dfrac{13}{20}$

Make sure you simplify them.

Round 1　　Circle the correct answers.

1. What is 0.3 as a fraction?	2. What is $\dfrac{3}{4}$ as a decimal?	3. What is 3.2 as a mixed number?	4. What is $2\dfrac{1}{5}$ as a decimal?
a) $\dfrac{1}{3}$	a) 0.25	a) $3\dfrac{3}{10}$	a) 2.5
b) $\dfrac{3}{10}$	b) 0.35	b) $3\dfrac{1}{2}$	b) 2.15
c) $\dfrac{3}{5}$	c) 0.75	c) $3\dfrac{1}{5}$	c) 2.2

Round 2

Write these as decimals:

1. $\dfrac{3}{100}$ = ☐

2. $\dfrac{1}{8}$ = ☐

Write these as fractions:

3. 0.07 = ☐

4. 0.45 = ☐

Round 3　　True or false? Circle your answer.

1. $1\dfrac{4}{5}$ is the same as 1.8

True / False?

2. 2.7 is the same as $2\dfrac{1}{7}$

True / False?

Worth 2 points

Simple percentages

Per cent (%) shows a fraction out of 100.

75% means 75 out of 100, or $\dfrac{75}{100} = \dfrac{3}{4}$

Per cent means out of 100.

Round 1

Circle the percentage of each shape that is shaded.

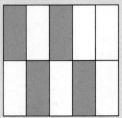

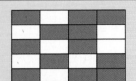

1.	2.	3.	4.
a) 4%	a) 50%	a) 12%	a) 20%
b) 60%	b) 5%	b) 40%	b) 40%
c) 40%	c) 20%	c) 60%	c) 80%

Round 2

Write these fractions as percentages:

1. $\dfrac{14}{25} = \boxed{}$ %

2. $\dfrac{4}{5} = \boxed{}$ %

Write these percentages as fractions:

3. $30\% = \boxed{}$

4. $25\% = \boxed{}$

Round 3

These are Sam's scores in a 'beat the goalie' penalty shoot-out against his sister.

 3 out of 5
 15 out of 20
6 out of 12
7 out of 10

Which score gave Sam his highest percentage?

Worth 2 points

 10
 9
 8
 7
 6
 5
 4
 3
 2
 1

Fractions, decimals and percentages

Fraction	$\frac{1}{2}$	$\frac{1}{4}$	$\frac{3}{4}$	$\frac{1}{5}$	$\frac{1}{10}$
Decimal	0.5	0.25	0.75	0.2	0.1
Percentage	50%	25%	75%	20%	10%

$$\frac{1}{4} = 0.25 = 25\%$$

 How many bottles did you get?

Round 1 Circle the correct answers.

1. What is 0.6 as a percentage?

a) 6%

b) 40%

c) 60%

2. What is 80% as a fraction?

a) $\frac{1}{8}$

b) $\frac{4}{5}$

c) $\frac{2}{5}$

3. What is $\frac{7}{10}$ as a percentage?

a) 70%

b) 17%

c) 7%

4. What is 0.45 as a percentage?

a) 55%

b) 40%

c) 45%

Round 2 Complete these.

1. $\frac{2}{5} = 0.4 = \boxed{}\%$

2. $\frac{3}{10} = 0.\boxed{} = \boxed{}\%$

3. $\frac{1}{\boxed{}} = 0.\boxed{} = 25\%$

4. $\frac{\boxed{}}{10} = 0.9 = \boxed{}\%$

Round 3 Circle each number that is less than 40%.

0.15   85%   50%   0.7

$\frac{1}{2}$ $\frac{1}{3}$ $\frac{3}{4}$

Worth 2 points

Percentages of quantities

Use 1% and 10% to help work out other percentages.

1% of 400g is 4g
↓
2% of 400g is 8g

3% of 400g is 12g

10% of 80p is 8p
↓
5% of 80p is 4p

20% of 80p is 16p

Circle the correct answer.

Use 1% and 10% to help you.

1. What is 5% of £6?
a) 60p
b) £3
c) 30p

2. What is 20% of 300ml?
a) 150ml
b) 60ml
c) 15ml

3. What is 2% of 1000g?
a) 200g
b) 20g
c) 50g

4. What is 30% of 50p?
a) 15p
b) 5p
c) 20p

Answer these.

1. A camera costs £140. There is 20% off in the sale. What is the sale price of the camera? ☐

2. A chocolate bar weighs 80g. The weight is increased by 25%. What is the new weight of the bar? ☐

3. In a sale, a coat is reduced from £45 by 10%. What is its new price? ☐

4. A Christmas card costs £1.20, with 5% of the cost going to charity. How much money will go to charity from this card? ☐

Match a label to each sale sign.   Worth 2 points

Was £20
Now £16

Was £30
Now £21

Was £40
Now £24

Was £50
Now £25

Sale
30%
OFF

Sale
40%
OFF

Sale
50%
OFF

Sale
20%
OFF

Mental addition

Breaking up numbers into sums can help you add numbers mentally.

73 + 48 is the same as

73 + 40 + 8 ⟶ 113 + 8

which is 121

 **Round 1** Choose the correct missing numbers.

1. 52 + 39 = ☐   **2.** ☐ + 38 = 67   **3.** 48 + ☐ = 94   **4.** 86 + 39 = ☐

a) 81   a) 105   a) 46   a) 117
b) 89   b) 29   b) 54   b) 107
c) 91   c) 39   c) 56   c) 125

Try to do these sums in your head.

 Round 2 Write the answers in the boxes.

Three children weigh 38kg, 51kg and 46kg.

If they stand on weighing scales, what four weights can they make, apart from 38kg, 51kg and 46kg?

☐ kg   ☐ kg

☐ kg   ☐ kg

 **Round 3** Complete these super squares. (*Worth 2 points*)

+17

+12

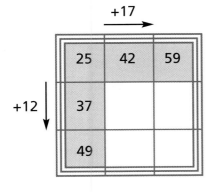

25	42	59
37		
49		

+17

+18

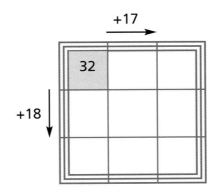

32		

10 9 8 7 6 5 4 3 2 1

Adding 3-digit numbers

Rounding numbers may be a good way to add in your head. If it is too difficult to add mentally, use a written method.

$$\begin{array}{r} 261 \\ + 358 \end{array}$$ is the same as $$\begin{array}{r} 260\ (+1) \\ + 360\ (-2) \\ \hline 620\ (-1) \end{array}$$

which is the same as 620 - 1 = 619

 Circle the correct totals.

1. 124 + 137

a) 251

b) 263

c) 261

2. 210 + 181

a) 300

b) 400

c) 391

3. 175 + 263

a) 428

b) 438

c) 338

4. 284 + 164

a) 448

b) 429

c) 349

 Use these numbers to answer the questions.

193	265
186	143
271	208

1. Which two numbers total 473? ☐ and ☐

2. What is the sum of the even numbers? ☐

3. Which three numbers total 600? ☐ ☐ ☐

4. What is the sum of the numbers in the left-hand column? ☐

 Circle the two weights with the same total.

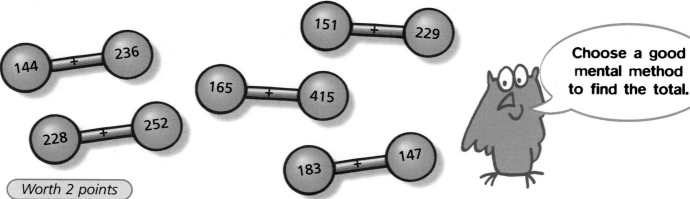

144 + 236

228 + 252

151 + 229

165 + 415

183 + 147

Choose a good mental method to find the total.

Worth 2 points

Adding large numbers

If you are adding numbers on paper using a 'vertical' method, remember to line up the units, then the other columns.

745 + 1489 + 2038

```
  2038
  1489
+  745
  4272
  1 1 2
```

Round 1 — Circle the correct answers.

1. What is the total of 2710, 2720 and 2730?

a) 7260

b) 8160

c) 8260

2. Which pair of numbers totals 4935?

a) 2074 + 2821

b) 3628 + 1267

c) 2477 + 2458

3. What is the sum of 1694 and 2008?

a) 3702

b) 3692

c) 3712

4. Which pair of numbers totals 5205?

a) 2119 + 3086

b) 1493 + 4292

c) 3714 + 2519

Round 2 — Write the missing digits for each of these.

1.
```
  3 1 □ 8
+ 2 8 7 4
  □ 0 4 2
```

2.
```
  6 4 8 1
+ 1 □ 6 4
  7 7 □ 5
```

3.
```
  2 0 7 □
+ 3 1 2 5
  5 □ 0 4
```

4.
```
  1 2 8 4
+ 4 8 3 □
  □ 1 2 1
```

Round 3 — Complete this number puzzle.

Across

1. 7000 + 8121

4. 2425 + 8550

5. 9300 + 4381

Down

1. 8401 + 9770

2. 9587 + 7359

3. 6058 + 6443

Worth 2 points

1		2		3
	5	1		
8		6		2
4	0		7	
7		4		0
5	3		8	

Adding decimals

Some additions can be done mentally.

If you need to write it down, line up the decimal points.

If the question is about money, make sure the pound sign goes in the answer.

$$
\begin{array}{r}
3.04 \\
21.65 \\
0.28 \\
\hline
24.97 \\
\hline
\end{array}
$$

Round 1   Circle the correct totals.

1. 4.3 + 8.16	**2.** 0.68 + 2.05	**3.** 16.4 + 9.37	**4.** 12.08 + 6.7
a) 12.46	**a)** 3.18	**a)** 25.41	**a)** 18.78
b) 12.19	**b)** 3.13	**b)** 26.77	**b)** 18.15
c) 13.1	**c)** 2.73	**c)** 25.77	**c)** 18.87

> **See if you can do these in your head.**

Round 2   Work out the total costs for these items for camping.

tent
£84.25

stove
£14.05

1. tent + rucksack + stove
2. sleeping bag + walking boots
3. rucksack + sleeping bag
4. walking boots + stove + rucksack

walking boots
£32.40

rucksack
£16.38

sleeping bag
£19.69

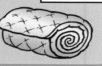

Round 3   These pieces of wood were all cut from the same length.

1.28m

1. What was the total length of the original piece of wood? ☐ m

2. The two longest pieces of wood are used to edge a 3 metre work top. How much extra wood is needed? ☐ cm

Worth 2 points

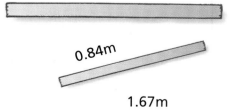
0.84m

1.67m

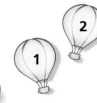

Mental subtraction

Counting on is a good way of subtracting mentally.

For example: 84 – 37

Count on from 37 to 40.

Hold 3 in your head. 40 on to 84 is 44.

Add 3 to 44, which is 47.

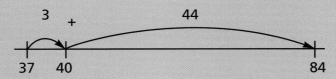

3 + 44

37 40 84

Count on from the lower number to the higher one.

Round 1

Choose the correct missing numbers.

1. 63 – 48 = ☐
a) 25
b) 15
c) 21

2. 71 – ☐ = 43
a) 28
b) 32
c) 22

3. ☐ – 29 = 47
a) 82
b) 76
c) 66

4. 86 – 58 = ☐
a) 32
b) 28
c) 38

Round 2

Use these numbers to answer the questions.

73	38
29	85
67	92

1. Which two numbers have a difference of 18? ☐ and ☐
2. What is the difference between the largest and smallest numbers? ☐
3. Which two numbers have a difference of 54? ☐ and ☐
4. Which two numbers give the smallest difference? ☐ and ☐

Round 3

Complete these subtraction grids.

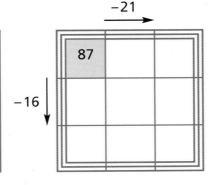

–18

74	56	38
65		
56		

–9

–21

87		

–16

Worth 2 points

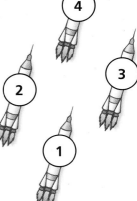

21

Subtracting 3-digit numbers

When you are asked to find the difference,
take the smaller number away from the bigger number.

Try counting on from the smaller number to find the difference.

 **Round 1**

Subtract 345 from each of these numbers.
Circle the correct answer for each.

1. 603	**2.** 518	**3.** 438	**4.** 762
a) 342	a) 273	a) 113	a) 417
b) 252	b) 173	b) 93	b) 423
c) 258	c) 233	c) 103	c) 427

 **Round 2**

Find the difference between these pairs of numbers.

1. 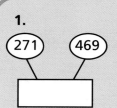 271 469

2. 193 506

3. 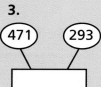 471 293

4. 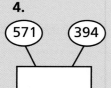 571 394

 **Round 3**

Complete this number puzzle.

Across

A 749 – 458
B 282 – 214
C 371 – 347
D 618 – 291
G 243 – 159
H 530 – 261

Down

A 514 – 311
B 800 – 157
E 432 – 168
F 609 – 530

Worth 2 points

Subtracting large numbers

If you are subtracting large numbers on paper you could use a method called decomposition.

$$
\begin{array}{r}
{\scriptstyle 4\ 12\ 7\ 13} \\
\cancel{5283} \\
-\ 2954 \\
\hline
2329 \\
\end{array}
$$

 Circle the correct answers.

1. What is the difference between 1984 and 3020?

a) 964

b) 1064

c) 1036

2. What is 2471 subtract 1185?

a) 1286

b) 1314

c) 1186

3. Which two numbers have a difference of 355?

a) 2077 and 2622

b) 3814 and 3559

c) 1938 and 2293

4. What is 6147 minus 2500?

a) 3647

b) 3547

c) 3653

Tick the number of stars you got right!

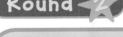

These are four of the highest mountains in Europe. Mount Everest in Nepal is the highest mountain in the world at 8846m. How much higher is it than these four mountains?

4505m — Weisshorn

4634m — Monte Rosa

4807m — Mont Blanc

4477m — Matterhorn

1. Weisshorn [ ]

2. Monte Rosa [ ]

3. Mont Blanc [ ]

4. Matterhorn [ ]

 Use the code to complete the message.

$$
\begin{array}{r}
5\ 9\ 0\ 1 \\
-\ 2\ 7\ 3\ 6 \\
\hline
\Box\ \Box\ \Box\ \Box \\
\end{array}
$$

$$
\begin{array}{r}
3\ 0\ 0\ 0\ 0 \\
-\ \ \ 4\ 8\ 6\ 2 \\
\hline
\Box\ \Box\ \Box\ \Box\ \Box \\
\end{array}
$$

1	2	3	4	5	6	7	8	9
A	B	C	D	E	F	G	H	I

Meet at the _ _ _ _ by the _ _ _ _ _

Worth 2 points

10   9   8   7   6   5   4   3   2   1

23

Subtracting decimals

Subtracting decimals is just like subtracting whole numbers, you just have to remember to line up the decimal points.

Round 1   Circle the difference between these pairs of numbers.

Always line up the decimal points.

1. 3.8 5.7	2. 5.05 2.6	3. 4.91 7.2	4. 0.6 1.42
a) 2.1	a) 2.45	a) 2.92	a) 1.22
b) 1.9	b) 3.01	b) 2.29	b) 0.78
c) 2.9	c) 2.55	c) 3.71	c) 0.82

Round 2   How much has the price of each pair of shoes been reduced by?

1. Original price: £38.49
   New price: £29.99
   Saving: £ [ ]

2. Original price: £51.50
   New price: £38.35
   Saving: £ [ ]

3. Original price: £34.85
   New price: £19.68
   Saving: £ [ ]

4. Original price: £61.29
   New price: £35.17
   Saving: £ [ ]

Round 3   Match the numbers with a difference of 5.5.

3.8   9.3   6.1   7.2

0.6   2.7   8.2

Write a number for the odd one out. [ ]

Multiplication: TU x U

To work out 38 x 6, break the 38 up into 30 and 8 and use the times tables to answer each part.

a) 30 x 6 = 180

b)   8 x 6 = 48

c) 180 + 48 = 228

Round 1   Circle the answers.

Use your times tables.

1. Circle the answer nearest to 350.

a) 38 x 9

b) 57 x 6

c) 71 x 5

2. Circle the answer nearest to 200.

a) 27 x 8

b) 42 x 5

c) 59 x 3

3. Circle the answer nearest to 400.

a) 54 x 7

b) 81 x 5

c) 67 x 6

4. Circle the answer nearest to 500.

a) 72 x 7

b) 98 x 5

c) 64 x 8

10

9

8

Round 2   Write the total weights for each of these multi-buy packs.

1.
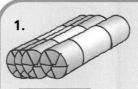

97g each

Total weight:

☐ g

2.
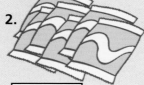

25g each

Total weight:

☐ g

3.

72g each

Total weight:

☐ g

4.

86g each

Total weight:

☐ g

7

6

5

4

Round 3

This recipe makes 8 flapjacks.

I need to make 32 flapjacks.

How much of each ingredient will I need?

Worth 2 points

Flapjacks (8)		Flapjacks (32)	
Oats	80g	Oats	☐ g
Butter	75g	Butter	☐ g
Sugar	62g	Sugar	☐ g
Flour	54g	Flour	☐ g
Syrup	28g	Syrup	☐ g

3

2

1

Multiplying large numbers

A grid method is one way of working out multiplication sums.

623 x 4

x	600	20	3
4	2400	80	12

2400 + 80 + 12 = 2492

Round 1

Circle the correct answer for each of these.

1. 371 x 5
a) 1535
b) 1855
c) 1750

2. 485 x 4
a) 1690
b) 1720
c) 1940

3. 614 x 6
a) 3664
b) 3724
c) 3684

4. 586 x 3
a) 1758
b) 1528
c) 1618

Round 2

Write the total capacity for each of these multi-buy packs.

1.
370ml
each
Total:
[ ] ml

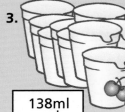

2.
985ml
each
Total:
[ ] ml

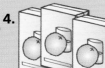
3.
138ml
each
Total:
[ ] ml

4.
755ml
each
Total:
[ ] ml

Round 3

Use these numbers to make a multiplication sum.

1. What is the largest possible product? [ ]

2. What is the smallest possible product? [ ]

Worth 2 points

 6 4

9 7

[ ][ ][ ]
X [ ]
_____

_____

10
9
8
7
6
5
4
3
2
1

Multiplication: TU x TU

Use the grid method to work out sums like these.
Always estimate the answer first.

47 x 36

x	30	6
40	1200	240
7	210	42

1440
+ 252
―――
1692

Check your answer by looking at your estimate.

Round 1 Circle the correct answer for each of these.

1. 51 x 64	**2.** 29 x 48	**3.** 67 x 35	**4.** 62 x 84
a) 3004	a) 1392	a) 1835	a) 4808
b) 3264	b) 1272	b) 2135	b) 4968
c) 3064	c) 872	c) 2345	c) 5208

Round 2 Calculate the area of each swimming pool.

1.
17m
25m

2.
15m
38m

3.
18m
12m

4.
16m
34m

Area = [   ] m²   Area = [   ] m²   Area = [   ] m²   Area = [   ] m²

Round 3 Use these numbers to make a multiplication sum.

4   **8**

3   **6**

X

1. What is the largest possible product?   [   ]

2. What is the smallest possible product?   [   ]

Worth 2 points

Multiplying decimals

Always estimate an approximate answer first.

21.89 x 4 is approximately 22 x 4 which is 88.

The actual answer is 87.56.

Round 1 Circle the correct answer for each of these.

1. 4.7 x 5	**2.** 6.8 x 4	**3.** 4.63 x 6	**4.** 8.07 x 9
a) 20.35	a) 27.2	a) 27.18	a) 72.16
b) 23.5	b) 24.32	b) 27.78	b) 78.3
c) 20.7	c) 25.2	c) 24.38	c) 72.63

Remember to round up or round down the decimal first when estimating.

Round 2 Work out the estimates and actual answers for these.

1.	Estimate	Answer	**2.**	Estimate	Answer
£3.45 x 4			£5.70 x 8		

3.	Estimate	Answer	**4.**	Estimate	Answer
£4.09 x 6			£7.61 x 3		

Round 3

Worth 2 points

Sam has £30 to spend on videos.

Which of these offers could he afford?

Tick the boxes.

Videos normal price £7.99

BARGAIN BUYS

Pack of 6 @ £4.99 each	
Pack of 8 @ £3.99 each	
Pack of 4 @ £6.99 each	

10
9
8
7
6
5
4
3
2
1

Division: TU ÷ U

Use the multiplication facts to help work out division facts.

| 7 x 4 = 28 | 28 ÷ 4 = 7 | 28 ÷ 7 = 4 |

Round 1

Circle the correct missing numbers.

1. 42 ÷ 6 = ☐

a) 9

b) 8

c) 7

2. 54 ÷ ☐ = 6

a) 9

b) 8

c) 7

3. 57 ÷ 3 = ☐

a) 17

b) 18

c) 19

4. 92 ÷ 4 = ☐

a) 21

b) 22

c) 23

> **Use the rules of multiplication to help you.**

Round 2

Look at these numbers to answer the questions.

73   95   84   86   72

1. Which of these numbers leaves a remainder of 1 when divided by 5? ☐

2. Which of these numbers divides exactly by 9? ☐

3. Which of these numbers leaves a remainder of 3 when divided by 4? ☐

4. Which of these numbers can be divided exactly by both 6 and 7? ☐

Round 3

Each number can be divided by one of these sets.
Use the code to find the names of two birds.

Number that can be divided by:	Code letter
7 and 4	O
4 and 6	W
7 and 9	C
3 and 5	R
6 and 9	N
7, 5 and 10	E

63 → ☐   48 → ☐

75 → ☐   45 → ☐

56 → ☐   70 → ☐

96 → ☐   54 → ☐

Worth 2 points

10

9

8

7

6

5

4

3

2

1

Long division: HTU ÷ TU

Always estimate an approximate answer first.

627 ÷ 19 is approximately 600 ÷ 20 which is 30.

The actual answer is 33.

Round 1 Circle the missing digit.

1.	2.	3.	4.
4 5 17 ⟌ 76 ☐	5 8 14 ⟌ 8 ☐ 2	2 7 16 ⟌ ☐ 3 2	3 9 18 ⟌ 7 ☐ 2
a) 3	a) 3	a) 5	a) 4
b) 5	b) 2	b) 3	b) 0
c) 8	c) 1	c) 4	c) 2

Check your answer by multiplying.

10

9

Round 2 Answer these.

1. Divide 345 by 15.

2. What is the remainder when 654 is divided by 13?

3. A video camera costs £846. How many weeks would it take to pay off that amount at £18 per week?

4. What is 612 divided by 12?

8

7

6

5

4

 **Round 3** Find the remainders.
Which ticket is the odd one out?

323 ÷ 23

511 ÷ 15

729 ÷ 28

267 ÷ 14

598 ÷ 18

3

2

1

Single-stage problems

| 1. Read the problem. | → | 2. Organise the calculation. | → | 3. Answer the calculation. | → | 4. Answer the problem. |

 **Round 1** Use the chart to find the correct answers and circle them.

Daily video rentals from the 'Video store'

Day	Number rented
Monday	74
Tuesday	89
Wednesday	106
Thursday	91
Friday	128
Saturday	167

1. How many more videos were rented on Wednesday than on Tuesday?
a) 16 b) 27 c) 17

2. What is the total number rented on Friday and Saturday?
a) 295 b) 285 c) 305

3. How many fewer videos were rented on Monday than on Thursday?
a) 27 b) 23 c) 17

4. What is the difference between the highest and lowest number of videos rented?
a) 83 b) 93 c) 113

 Round 2 These are the prices in a camera shop.

£73   album £4.90   £8.25 for 3   £28

1. What is the total price of a camera and tripod?

2. What is the price of four photo albums?

3. What is the price of one film?

4. If you bought 3 films, what change would you get from £10?

 Round 3 True or false? Circle your answer.

1. A train leaves London at 9.52am and arrives at Newark at 11.08am. The journey takes 1 hour 16 minutes.
True/False

2. The train takes a further 48 minutes from Newark to reach Leeds. It arrives at 11.54am.
True/False   (Worth 2 points)

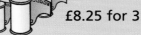

Two-stage problems

| 1. Read the problem. | → | 2. Organise the two calculations. | → | 3. Answer the calculations. | → | 4. Answer the problem. |

These are the prices to see a film at the cinema.
Circle the total price for each group.

Ritz Cinema

Adults – **£3.80**

Children – **£2.15**

1. 2 adults and 1 child
a) £8.95
b) £9.75
c) £5.95

2. 1 adult and 3 children
a) £10.15
b) £9.95
c) £10.25

3. 3 adults and 1 child
a) £13.45
b) £11.39
c) £13.55

4. 1 adult and 4 children
a) £1.40
b) £12.40
c) £12.20

Answer these.

1. David wants to buy four packets of stickers that cost 85p each. He has £3. How much more money does he need?

2. Six pencils laid end to end measure 84cm. What will ten pencils laid end to end measure?

3. Sid the window cleaner works 8 hours each day. If he averages two houses each hour, how many houses will he visit in five days?

4. A sausage roll costs 48p. What change would there be from £5 for 6 sausage rolls?

For an approximate conversion of miles to kilometres, multiply by 8 then divide by 5.

Convert these distances:

$miles \rightarrow \times 8 \rightarrow \div 5 \rightarrow km$

1. 20 miles = [   ] km

2. [   ] miles = 24 km

Worth 2 points

When you've found your answer, read the problem again to check it.

Three-stage problems

1. Read the problem.	→	2. Organise the calculations.	→	3. Answer the calculations.	→	4. Answer the problem.

A car journey costs 20p per mile. Use the mileage chart to calculate the correct cost of these journeys. Circle the correct answers.

Aberdeen

430	Birmingham		
465	110	Cambridge	
580	205	120	Dover

1. Aberdeen – Birmingham (return)   **a)** £430   **b)** £172   **c)** £215
2. Aberdeen – Cambridge – Dover   **a)** £255   **b)** £137   **c)** £117
3. Birmingham – Dover (return)   **a)** £82   **b)** £21   **c)** £85
4. Dover – Birmingham – Cambridge   **a)** £61   **b)** £610   **c)** £63

Answer these.

1. Natalie needs a score of 74. She throws a 20, a 15 and a 13. What score does she need now?

2. Sandwiches are 90p each and rolls are 75p each. What is the change from £10 for 5 sandwiches and 6 rolls?

3. Entrance to a swimming pool costs £2.90 for adults and £1.80 for children. What is the total cost for 3 adults and 4 children?

4. There are 5 sweets in a packet. 8 packets are put in a bag and 20 bags put in a box. How many sweets are in 6 boxes?

For an approximate conversion of degrees Celsius ($^{\circ}$C) to degrees Fahrenheit ($^{\circ}$F), multiply by 9, divide by 5, then add 32.

Convert these temperatures.

1. 50°C = ⬚ $^{\circ}$F

2. ⬚ $^{\circ}$C = 95°F

Celsius	→	x 9	→	÷ 5	→	+32	→	Fahrenheit

Worth 2 points

Make sure you use the right calculation.

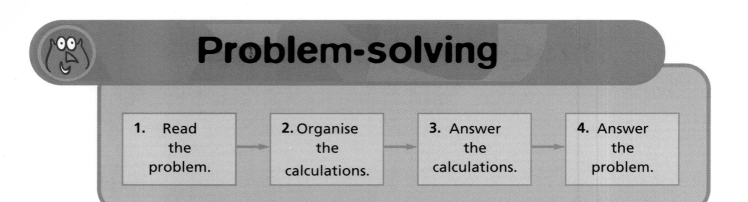

Problem-solving

1. Read the problem.	→	2. Organise the calculations.	→	3. Answer the calculations.	→	4. Answer the problem.

'Comfy Coach Company' offers these discounts for group bookings. Circle the total cost of each booking.

DISCOUNTS

10 – 15 seats: £1 per person

16 – 30 seats: £2 per person

31 – 50 seats: £3 per person

1. 12 seats: normal price £15 each

a) 178 b) £168 c) 180

2. 38 seats: normal price £9 each

a) £342 b) £266 c) £228

3. 25 seats: normal price £10 each

a) £250 b) £180 c) £200

4. 46 seats: normal price £15 each

a) £690 b) £552 c) £598

Work out the costs for each of these groups to go to the theme parks.

	Space Park — Adults: £12 Children: £5.50	Dino Land — Adults: £8.50 Children: £7	
Group	Cost: Space Park	Cost: Dino Land	Difference
1. 2 adults 2 children			
2. 5 adults 3 children			
3. 1 adult 6 children			
4. 4 adults 10 children			

Use a calculator. Calculate one year as 365 days.

1. If you sleep for 8 hours every night, how many hours will you have slept by the time you are 60? ☐ hours

2. How many years is this equivalent to? ☐ years

Worth 2 points

Mental maths: adding and subtracting

Always look at the numbers carefully. Do you know a mental strategy for adding or subtracting the numbers?

Round 1 Circle the correct answer.

Check your answer.

1. 53 + 38	2. 0.7 + 2.31	3. 84 − 27	4. 0.6 − 0.15
a) 81	a) 2.48	a) 63	a) 0.45
b) 91	b) 2.38	b) 57	b) 0.55
c) 89	c) 3.01	c) 67	c) 0.09

Round 2

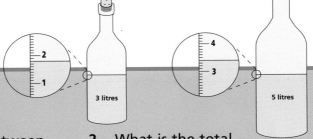

3 litres

5 litres

1. What is the difference between the amount of water in each bottle?

2. What is the total amount of water in the two bottles?

3. How much more water is needed to fill the 3 litre bottle?

4. How much more water is needed to fill the 5 litre bottle?

Round 3

Complete these 'super squares'.

− 18

56	38	
70		

+14

+1.7

7.3		

−2.6

Worth 2 points

Mental maths: using doubles

Use doubles to help with near-doubles.

34 + 34 = 68
34 + 35 = 69

Round 1 Circle the number which comes out of each doubling machine.

1. 27 → x 2 → ?

a) 44
b) 47
c) 54

2. 380 → x 2 → ?

a) 760
b) 640
c) 740

3. 0.19 → x 2 → ?

a) 0.28
b) 0.38
c) 3.8

4. 5.6 → x 2 → ?

a) 10.12
b) 11.2
c) 10.2

Round 2 What is the total cost for each pair of items?

Remember: work out the double, then adjust the answer.

1.

£1.14   £1.15

Total: [ ]

2.

74p   75p

Total: [ ]

3.

£1.28   £1.30

Total: [ ]

4.

69p   71p

Total: [ ]

Round 3 Write the missing numbers

1. start
23   x 2 [ ]   x 2 [ ]   END

2. start
0.17   x 2 [ ]   x 2 [ ]   END

3. start
140   x 2 [ ]   x 2 [ ]   END

4. start
1.8   x 2 [ ]   x 2 [ ]   END

Worth 2 points

10
9
8
7
6
5
4
3
2
1

Mentalmaths: counting on

To find the difference between numbers, count on.

To find the difference between 67 and 112, count on from 67.

3	30	12

67 70 | 3 + 30 + 12 is 45 | 100 112

Round 1 Circle the correct difference between these pairs of numbers.

1. 48 74	**2.** 117 84	**3.** 213 158	**4.** 9.2 6.7
a) 34	**a)** 33	**a)** 45	**a)** 3.5
b) 26	**b)** 23	**b)** 65	**b)** 2.5
c) 24	**c)** 27	**c)** 55	**c)** 3.2

Keep the numbers in your head.

Round 2 These are the heights of a group of children.

Name	Josh	Callum	Millie	Hannah	David	Stefan
Height	128cm	134cm	109cm	152cm	146cm	114cm

1. How much taller is Hannah than Millie? ☐

2. Who is 32cm taller than Stefan? ☐

3. Which two children have a difference in height of 25cm? ☐ and ☐

4. How much taller is David than Josh? ☐

Round 3

Donwick

Crothorpe   Eastly

42km   95km   77km

36km

Benby

Anton

Worth 2 points

1. How far is it from Benby to Donwick? ☐ km

2. How far is it from Anton to Eastly? ☐ km

10 9 8 7 6 5 4 3 2 1

Mental maths: inverses

Addition and subtraction and multiplication and division are opposites, or inverses.

Check your answers using inverses.

83 − 56 = 27	84 ÷ 3 = 28
27 + 56 = 83	28 x 3 = 84

Round 1 Choose the correct missing number.

1. ☐ + 17 = 53	2. 72 − ☐ = 28	3. ☐ ÷ 3 = 21	4. ☐ x 4 = 68
a) 70	a) 44	a) 7	a) 14
b) 44	b) 46	b) 67	b) 19
c) 36	c) 54	c) 63	c) 17

How many did you get right?

Round 2 Complete this number chain.
Check each step by looking at the inverse.

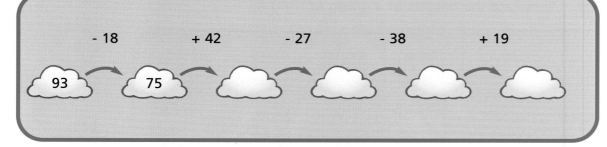

− 18   + 42   − 27   − 38   + 19

93   75

10 9 8 7 6 5 4 3 2 1

Round 3 Write the missing numbers coming out of this machine.

68
93
106

IN   −27   OUT

41

Worth 2 points

Round-up quiz

Circle the correct answer for each of the following statements.

Ready for the Round-up quiz?

A

1. The sum of 18 and 35 is
   - a) 43
   - b) 52
   - c) 53

2. The value of 5 in 2530 is
   - a) 50
   - b) 500
   - c) 5000

3. A multiple of 3 is
   - a) 42
   - b) 52
   - c) 62

4. $\frac{3}{4}$ is more than
   - a) $\frac{4}{5}$
   - b) $\frac{2}{3}$
   - c) $\frac{9}{10}$

5. Dividing 28 by 10 gives
   - a) 2
   - b) 0.28
   - c) 2.8

6. A square number is
   - a) 60
   - b) 49
   - c) 75

7. The difference between 45 and 29 is
   - a) 24
   - b) 16
   - c) 26

8. $\frac{8}{12}$ is equivalent to
   - a) $\frac{3}{4}$
   - b) $\frac{2}{3}$
   - c) $\frac{5}{6}$

9. 18 out of 20 in a test is:
   - a) 80%
   - b) 98%
   - c) 90%

10. The total of 0.3, 0.6 and 0.15 is
    - a) 1.5
    - b) 2.4
    - c) 1.05

Round-up quiz

Circle the correct answer for each of the following statements.

B

How are you doing?

1. Dividing 104 by 5 leaves a remainder of
   a) 1
   b) 4
   c) 2

2. In $3\frac{1}{2}$ minutes there are
   a) 150 seconds
   b) 180 seconds
   c) 210 seconds

3. $\frac{3}{5}$ is equivalent to
   a) 30%
   b) 60%
   c) 50%

4. Adding 99 to 234 equals
   a) 335
   b) 343
   c) 333

5. 7246 rounded to the nearest 100 is
   a) 7200
   b) 7300
   c) 7250

6. An odd multiple of 3 is
   a) 36
   b) 27
   c) 35

7. Multiplying 0.38 by 10 gives
   a) 38.0
   b) 3.8
   c) 10.38

8. 10 more than 3096 is
   a) 3196
   b) 3116
   c) 3106

9. The difference between -5°C and 4°C is
   a) 9°C
   b) 1°C
   c) 8°C

10. 4.7 is equivalent to
   a) $4\frac{1}{7}$
   b) $4\frac{10}{7}$
   c) $4\frac{7}{10}$

Round-up quiz

Circle the correct answer for each of the following statements.

Have you done them all?

C

1. A factor of 42 is
   a) 7
   b) 4
   c) 8

2. The value of 3 in 63045 is
   a) 300
   b) 3000
   c) 30000

3. 10 more than 4.8 is
   a) 48.0
   b) 14.8
   c) 4.18

4. $3\frac{1}{4}$ metres is the same as:
   a) 325cm
   b) 340cm
   c) 3.25cm

5. 17.81 is 2 less than
   a) 17.61
   b) 15.81
   c) 19.81

6. Multiplying 0.68 by 10 gives
   a) 68
   b) 1.68
   c) 6.8

7. 8/100 is equivalent to
   a) 0.8
   b) 8.1
   c) 0.08

8. The product of 12 and 6 is
   a) 2
   b) 72
   c) 18

9. 0.3 litres is the same as
   a) 30ml
   b) 300ml
   c) 3ml

10. $3\frac{2}{5}$ is the same as
   a) $\frac{17}{5}$
   b) $\frac{6}{5}$
   c) $\frac{6}{15}$

Key facts 1

Multiplication table

x	1	2	3	4	5	6	7	8	9	10
1	1	2	3	4	5	6	7	8	9	10
2	2	4	6	8	10	12	14	16	18	20
3	3	6	9	12	15	18	21	24	27	30
4	4	8	12	16	20	24	28	32	36	40
5	5	10	15	20	25	30	35	40	45	50
6	6	12	18	24	30	36	42	48	54	60
7	7	14	21	28	35	42	49	56	63	70
8	8	16	24	32	40	48	56	64	72	80
9	9	18	27	36	45	54	63	72	81	90
10	10	20	30	40	50	60	70	80	90	100

Averages

There are three types of average:

mean = $\dfrac{\text{total number of items}}{\text{number of items used}}$

median = the middle value when the numbers are ranged in order of size

mode = the number that occurs most often

Square, triangle and prime numbers to 100

Square numbers	1	4	19	16	25	36	49	64	81	100	121	144	169
Triangle numbers	1	3	6	10	15	21	28	36	45	55	66	78	91
Prime numbers	2 43	3 47	5 53	7 59	11 61	13 67	17 71	19 73	23 79	29 83	31 89	37 97	41

Fractions, decimals and percentages

Fraction	$\frac{1}{2}$	$\frac{1}{4}$	$\frac{3}{4}$	$\frac{1}{5}$	$\frac{1}{10}$	$\frac{1}{8}$	$\frac{1}{3}$	$\frac{2}{3}$
Decimal	0.5	0.25	0.75	0.2	0.1	0.125	0.333	0.666
%	50%	25%	75%	20%	10%	$12\frac{1}{2}$%	$33\frac{1}{3}$%	$66\frac{2}{3}$%

Key facts 2

3D shapes

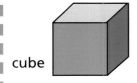 cube

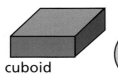 cuboid

 cylinder

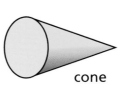 cone

 sphere

 triangular-based pyramid

2D shapes – circle facts

- the circumference is all the way round the circle
- the diameter is twice the radius

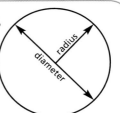

Number of sides	3	4	5	6	7	8	9	10
Name of polygon	triangle	quadrilateral	pentagon	hexagon	heptagon	octagon	nonagon	decagon

Measurements

1000g = 1kg	10mm = 1cm	milli thousandth	10ml = 1cl
	100cm = 1m	deci tenth	10cl = 1dl
1000kg = 1 tonne	1000mm = 1m	centi hundredth	100cl = 1 litre
	1000m = 1km	kilo thousand	100ml = 1dl
			1000ml = 1 litre

Time

a.m.   p.m.

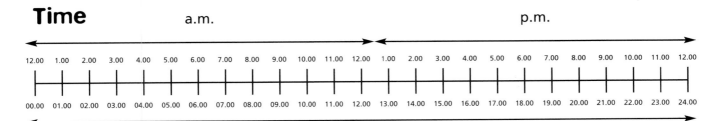

24-hour time

Quiz scores: record grid

You can use this chart to keep a record of your scores for every page, and your running total. There are ten points available on each page.

Page	Activities	My scores	My running total	Maximum score
6	Multiplying and dividing by 10 and 100			10
7	Ordering numbers			20
8	Estimating and rounding numbers			30
9	Negative numbers			40
10	Equivalent fractions			50
11	Ordering and simplifying fractions			60
12	Improper fractions			70
13	Fractions and decimals			80
14	Simple percentages			90
15	Fractions, decimals and percentages			100
16	Percentages of quantities			110
17	Mental addition			120
18	Adding 3-digit numbers			130
19	Adding large numbers			140
20	Adding decimals			150
21	Mental subtraction			160
22	Subtracting 3-digit numbers			170
23	Subtracting large numbers			180
24	Subtracting decimals			190
25	Multiplication: TU x U			200
26	Multiplying large numbers			210

Page	Activities	My scores	My runing total	Maximum score
27	Multiplication: TU x TU			220
28	Multiplying decimals			230
29	Division: TU ÷ U			240
30	Long division: HTU ÷ TU			250
31	Single-stage problems			260
32	Two-stage problems			270
33	Three-stage problems			280
34	Problem solving			290
35	Mental maths: adding and subtracting			300
36	Mental maths: using doubles			310
37	Mental maths: counting on			320
38	Mental maths: inverses			330
39	Round-up quiz A			340
40	Round-up quiz B			350
41	Round-up quiz C			360

If you want to, you can agree some rewards with your parents for reaching these scores as you work through the book!

Points	Rewards
60	
120	
180	
240	
300	
360	

Answers

page 6 Multiplying and dividing by 10 and 100
Round 1
1. c) 340   2. a) 47
3. c) 760   4. b) 8.02
Round 2
1. 67   2. 190
3. 100   4. 100
Round 3
720, 1.5

page 7 Ordering numbers
Round 1
1. b) 739   2. c) 4803
3. b) 62180   4. a) 2.4
Round 2
1. 214, 241, 271, 301, 311
2. 6251, 60520, 61205, 62051, 63001
3. 4080, 4111, 4180, 4208, 4810
4. 6.4, 6.45, 6.8, 7.21, 7.7
Round 3
5160 > 5061 < 5106 < 5601 < 5610
> 5016

page 8 Estimating and rounding numbers
Round 1
1. c) 56   2. b) 340
3. b) 2565   4. c) 2.56
Round 2
1. 170   2. 620
3. 630   4. 460
Round 3
1. False   2. False

page 9 Negative numbers
Round 1
1. a) 14°C   2. a) 3°C
3. c) -1°C   4. b) -15°C
Round 2
1. 7°C   2. 5°C
3. 6°C   4. 12°C
Round 3
1. -2, -4   2. -5, -7

page 10 Equivalent fractions
Round 1
1. c) $\frac{4}{6}$ 2. a) $\frac{6}{8}$

3. c) $\frac{2}{8}$ 4. c) $\frac{10}{12}$

Round 2
1. $\frac{9}{12}$, $\frac{3}{4}$ 2. $\frac{2}{3}$, $\frac{8}{12}$

Round 3
1. $\frac{3}{12}$ 2. $\frac{16}{30}$

page 11 Ordering and simplifying fractions
Round 1
1. c) $\frac{1}{4}$ 2. b) $\frac{3}{5}$

2. b) $\frac{3}{4}$ 4. a) $\frac{2}{3}$

Round 2
1. $\frac{1}{4}$ $\frac{1}{2}$ $\frac{5}{8}$ $\frac{3}{4}$

2. $\frac{1}{3}$ $\frac{7}{12}$ $\frac{2}{3}$ $\frac{5}{6}$

3. $\frac{8}{15}$ $\frac{3}{5}$ $\frac{7}{10}$ $\frac{4}{5}$

4. $\frac{3}{8}$ $\frac{12}{24}$ $\frac{7}{12}$ $\frac{5}{6}$

Round 3
1. Hannah   2. Ben

page 12 Improper fractions
Round 1
1. c) $\frac{8}{5}$ 2. a) $\frac{11}{4}$

3. b) $\frac{5}{3}$ 4. b) $\frac{23}{6}$

Round 2
1. 14 2. 2 3. 23 4. 1
Round 3
Mouse $\frac{23}{6}$ matches to computer $3\frac{5}{6}$

Mouse $\frac{19}{5}$ matches to computer $3\frac{4}{5}$

page 13 Fractions and decimals
Round 1
1. b) $\frac{3}{10}$ 2. c) 0.75

3. c) $3\frac{1}{5}$ 4. c) 2.2

Round 2
1. 0.03   3. $\frac{7}{100}$

2. 0.125   4. $\frac{45}{100}$ or $\frac{9}{20}$

Round 3
1. True   2. False

page 14 Simple percentages
Round 1
1. c) 40%   2. a) 50%
3. c) 60%   4. a) 20%
Round 2
1. 56%   2. 80%
3. $\frac{3}{10}$ or $\frac{30}{100}$ 4. $\frac{1}{4}$ or $\frac{25}{100}$
Round 3
15 out of 20

page 15 Fractions, decimals and percentages
Round 1
1. c) 60%   2. b) $\frac{4}{5}$
3. a) 70%   4. c) 45%

Round 2
1. $\frac{2}{5}$ = 0.4 = 40%   2. $\frac{3}{10}$ = 0.3 = 30%

3. $\frac{1}{4}$ = 0.25 = 25%   4. $\frac{9}{10}$ = 0.9 = 90%

Round 3
0.15, $\frac{1}{3}$

page 16 Percentages of quantities
Round 1
1. c) 30p   2. b) 60ml
3. b) 20g   4. a) 15p
Round 2
1. £112   3. £40.50
2. 100g   4. 6p or £0.06

46

Round 3

30% off ➝ Was £30, Now £21
40% off ➝ Was £40, Now £24
50% off ➝ Was £50, Now £25
20% off ➝ Was £20, Now £16

page 17 Mental addition

Round 1
1. c) 91
2. b) 29
3. a) 46
4. c) 125

Round 2
89kg, 84kg, 97kg, 135kg

Round 3

25	42	59		32	49	66
37	54	71		50	67	84
49	66	83		68	85	102

page 18 Adding 3-digit numbers

Round 1
1. c) 261
2. c) 391
3. b) 438
4. a) 448

Round 2
1. 265 and 208
2. 394
3. 186, 143, 271
4. 650

Round 3
144 + 236 and 151 + 229

page 19 Adding large numbers

Round 1
1. b) 8160
2. c) 2477 + 2458
3. a) 3702
4. a) 2119 + 3086

Round 2

1. 3 1 ⑥ 8
   + 2 8 7 4
   ⑥ 0 4 2

2. 6 4 8 1
   + 1 ② 6 4
   7 7 ④ 5

3. 2 0 7 ⑨
   + 3 1 2 5
   5 ② 0 4

4. 1 2 8 4
   + 4 8 3 ⑦
   ⑥ 1 2 1

Round 3

1	5	1	2	1
8		6		2
1	0	9	7	5
7		4		0
1	3	6	8	1

page 20 Adding decimals

Round 1
1. a) 12.46
2. c) 2.73
3. c) 25.77
4. a) 18.78

Round 2
1. £114.68
2. £52.09
3. £36.07
4. £62.83

Round 3
1. 3.79m
2. 5cm

page 21 Mental subtraction

Round 1
1. b) 15
2. a) 28
3. b) 76
4. b) 28

Round 2
1. 67, 85
2. 63
3. 38, 92
4. 67, 73

Round 3

74	56	38		87	66	45
65	47	29		71	50	29
56	38	20		55	34	13

page 22 Subtracting 3-digit numbers

Round 1
1. c) 258
2. b) 173
3. b) 93
4. a) 417

Round 2
1. 198
2. 313
3. 178
4. 177

Round 3

page 23 Subtracting large numbers

Round 1
1. c) 1036
2. a) 1286
3. c) 1938 and 2293
4. a) 3647

Round 2
1. 4341m
2. 4212m
3. 4039m
4. 4369m

Round 3
Meet at the cafe by the beach

page 24 Subtracting decimals

Round 1
1. b) 1.9
2. a) 2.45
3. b) 2.29
4. c) 0.82

Round 2
1. £8.50
2. £13.15
3. £15.17
4. £26.12

Round 3
3.8 and 9.3; 6.1 and
0.6; 8.2 and 2.7

The odd number out is 7.2
The new number needed is 1.7
as 7.2 and 1.7 have a difference
of 5.5.

page 25 Multiplication: TU x U

Round 1
1. c) 71 x 5
2. b) 42 x 5
3. c) 67 x 6
4. a) 72 x 7

Round 2
1. 388g
2. 150g
3. 360g
4. 344g

Round 3
Oats 320g, butter 300g, sugar
248g, flour 216g, syrup 112g

page 26 Multiplying large numbers

Round 1
1. b) 1855
2. c) 1940
3. c) 3684
4. a) 1758

Round 2
1. 2220ml
2. 3940ml
3. 1242ml
4. 2265ml

Round 3
1. 764 x 9 = 6876
2. 679 x 4 = 2716

page 27 Multiplication: TU x TU

Round 1
1. b) 3264
2. a) 1392
3. c) 2345
4. c) 5208

Round 2
1. 425m²
2. 570m²
3. 216m²
4. 544m²

Round 3
1. 83 x 64 = 5312
2. 36 x 48 = 1728

page 28 Multiplying decimals

Round 1
1. b) 23.5
2. a) 27.2
3. b) 27.78
4. c) 72.63

Round 2
1. Estimate £12, Answer £13.80
2. Estimate £48, Answer £45.60
3. Estimate £24, Answer £24.54
4. Estimate £24, Answer £22.83

Round 3
Sam could afford 6 @ £4.99 or
4 @ £6.99

---

page 29 Division: TU ÷ U

Round 1
1. c) 7   2. a) 9   3. c) 19   4. c) 23

Round 2
1. 86   2. 72   3. 95   4. 84

Round 3
Crow and wren

---

page 30 Long division: HTU ÷ TU

Round 1
1. b) 5   2. c) 1   3. c) 4   4. b) 0

Round 2
1. 23   2. 4   3. 47 weeks   4. 51

Round 3
Odd one out is 598 ÷ 18
This has a remainder of 4.
The others have a
remainder of 1.

---

page 31 Single-stage problems

Round 1
1. c) 17   2. a) 295   3. c) 17   4. b) 93

Round 2
1. £101.00   2. £19.60
3. £2.75   4. £1.75

Round 3
1. True   2. False

---

page 32 Two-stage problems

Round 1
1. b) £9.75   2. c) £10.25
3. c) £13.55   4. b) £12.40

Round 2
1. £0.40 or 40p
2. 140cm or 1m 40cm
3. 80 houses
4. £2.12

Round 3
1. 32km   2. 15 miles

---

page 33 Three-stage problems

Round 1
1. b) £172   2. c) £117
3. a) £82   4. c) £63

Round 2
1. 26   2. £1
3. £15.90   4. 4800 sweets

Round 3
1. 122°F   2. 35°C

---

page 34 Problem solving

Round 1
1. b) £168   2. c) £228
3. c) £200   4. b) £552

Round 2
1. Space Park £35; Dino Land £31;
difference £4

2. Space Park £76.50; Dino Land
£63.50; difference £13

3. Space Park £45; Dino Land
£50.50; difference £5.50

4. Space Park £103; Dino Land
£104; difference £1

Round 3
1. 175 200 hours   2. 20 years

---

page 35 Mental maths: adding
and subtracting

Round 1
1. b) 91   2. c) 3.01
3. b) 57   4. a) 0.45

Round 2
1. 1.6 litres   2. 5.2 litres
3. 1.2 litres   4. 1.6 litres

Round 3
56   38   20   7.3   9.0   10.7
70   52   34   4.7   6.4   8.1
84   66   48   2.1   3.8   5.5

---

page 36 Mental maths: using
doubles

Round 1
1. c) 54   2. a) 760
3. b) 0.38   4. b) 11.2

Round 2
1. £2.29   2. £1.49
3. £2.58   4. £1.40

Round 3
1. 46, 92   2. 0.34, 0.68
3. 280, 560   4. 3.6, 7.2

---

page 37 Mental maths: counting on

Round 1
1. b) 26   2. a) 33
3. c) 55   4. b) 2.5

Round 2
1. 43cm   2. David
3. Callum and Millie 4. 18cm

Round 3
1. 137km   2. 250km

---

page 38 Mental maths: inverses

Round 1
1. c) 36   2. a) 44
3. c) 63   4. c) 17

Round 2
117 ➤ 90 ➤ 52 ➤ 71

Round 3
66, 79

---

page 39 Round-up quiz

A
1. c) 53   2. b) 500   3. a) 42
4. b) $\frac{2}{3}$ 5. c) 2.8

6. b) 49   7. b) 16   8. b) $\frac{2}{3}$
9. c) 90%   10. c) 1.05

---

page 40 Round-up quiz

B
1. b) 4   2. c) 210 seconds
3. b) 60%   4. c) 333
5. a) 7200

6. b) 27   7. b) 3.8
8. c) 3106   9. A) 9°C
10. c) $4\frac{7}{10}$

---

page 41 Round-up quiz

C
1. a) 7   2. b) 3000
3. b) 14.8   4. a) 325cm
5. c) 19.81

6. c) 6.8   7. c) 0.08
8. b) 72   9. b) 300ml
10. a) $\frac{17}{5}$